The Best of Tammy Wynette

Project Manager: Carol Cuellar
Cover Design: Thais Yanes

WARNER BROS. PUBLICATIONS - THE GLOBAL LEADER IN PRINT
USA: 15800 NW 48th Avenue, Miami, FL 33014

WARNER/CHAPPELL MUSIC

NUOVA CARISCH

INTERNATIONAL MUSIC PUBLICATIONS LIMITED

CANADA: 85 SCARSDALE ROAD, SUITE 101
DON MILLS, ONTARIO, M3B 2R2
SCANDINAVIA: P.O. BOX 533, VENDEVAGEN 85 B
S-182 15, DANDERYD, SWEDEN
AUSTRALIA: P.O. BOX 353
3 TALAVERA ROAD, NORTH RYDE N.S.W. 2113

ITALY: VIA CAMPANIA, 12
20098 S. GIULIANO MILANESE (MI)
ZONA INDUSTRIALE SESTO ULTERIANO
SPAIN: MAGALLANES, 25
28015 MADRID
FRANCE: 25 RUE DE HAUTEVILLE, 75010 PARIS

ENGLAND: SOUTHEND ROAD,
WOODFORD GREEN, ESSEX IG8 8HN
GERMANY: MARSTALLSTR. 8, D-80539 MUNCHEN
DENMARK: DANMUSIK, VOGNMAGERGADE 7
DK 1120 KOBENHAVNK

Recorded by TAMMY WYNETTE

STAND BY YOUR MAN

Words and Music by
TAMMY WYNETTE and BILLY SHERRILL

Stand by Your Man - 2 - 1

Recorded by TAMMY WYNETTE

SINGING MY SONG

Words and Music by
TAMMY WYNETTE, BILLY SHERRIL
and GLENN SUTTON

Singing My Song - 2 - 1

Recorded by TAMMY WYNETTE

RUN, WOMAN, RUN

Words and Music by
ANN BOOTH, DUKE GOFF and DAN HOFFMAN

Slowly

To-day's the day____ you're tell-ing him that he's got to set you
young girl,____ so un-der- stand it's so hard to find a

free And that be - in'____ one man's wom- an____ brings you
man Who comes home____ ev - 'ry night____ to on - ly

down.____ But be - fore____ you throw a -
you. You may not find____ true love a -

Run, Woman, Run - 2 - 1

Recorded by TAMMY WYNETTE

TAKE ME TO YOUR WORLD

Words and Music by
BILLY SHERRILL and GLENN SUTTON

Take Me to Your World - 2 - 1

Recorded by TAMMY WYNETTE

I'LL SEE HIM THROUGH

Words and Music by
NORRIS WILSON and BILLY SHERRILL

Some-times I won-der if he loves me like he used to So

man-y things bring doubt___ to my mind. It's on-ly nat-u-ral for a

wom-an___ to sit and wor-ry And search for all the faults___ she can

find. Last night I wait-ed up It seemed for-ev-er

Recorded by TAMMY WYNETTE

MY MAN

Words and Music by
NORRIS WILSON, CARMOL TAYLOR
and BILLY SHERRILL

Recorded by TAMMY WYNETTE

KIDS
(Say The Darndest Things)

Words and Music by
BILLY SHERRILL and GLENN SUTTON

Kids - 4 - 1

Lyrics:

four - year - old said, " I want a div - orce". Now, where did she hear that? —
"Mom-my, Dad-dy's tell-in' some-one on the phone: — 'Don't you call me here no more'. —

Kids say the darn - dest things. — Have you ev - er lis - tened close to the games — they play — or the lit - tle songs — they sing? —

Kids - 4 - 2

18

"Bet my____ dad-dy can whip your dad-dy; but dad-dy's nev-er home.____

____ And I think mom-my's wor-ried 'bout him 'cause

she cried all night long."

Kids say the darn-dest things.____ Have you

Recorded by TAMMY WYNETTE

GOOD LOVIN'
(Makes It Right)

Words and Music by
BILLY SHERRILL

Lyrics:

Good lov-in' keeps a home to-geth—er,

Good lov-in' sure can make it right.

If you nev-er want to be with-out— him, it means lov-in' ev-'ry-

thing a-bout— him, And that keeps your man— a-round at night.___

To Coda

Recorded by TAMMY WYNETTE

THE WAYS TO LOVE A MAN

Words and Music by
TAMMY WYNETTE, BILLY SHERRILL
and GLENN SUTTON

There are so man-y ways to love a man, and so man-y things to un-der-stand. And if there ev-er comes a time you de-cide to change your mind, I'll need a way to

The Ways to Love a Man - 3 - 1

Recorded by TAMMY WYNETTE

ANOTHER LONELY SONG

Words and Music by
BILLY SHERRILL, GLENN SUTTON
and TAMMY WYNETTE

Another Lonely Song - 3 - 1

28

Recorded by TAMMY WYNETTE

ONE OF A KIND

Words and Music by
BILLY SHERRILL and STEVE DAVIS

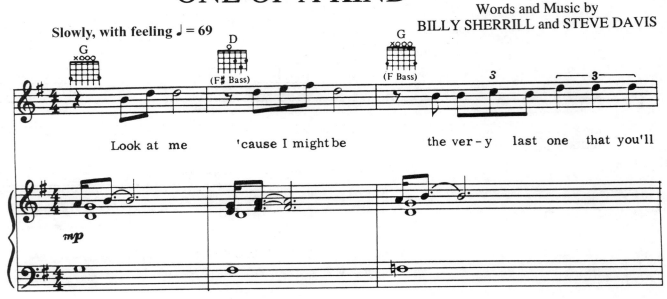

Look at me 'cause I might be the ver-y last one that you'll

ev - er see. Some-day you may wake up and find I'm one__ of a

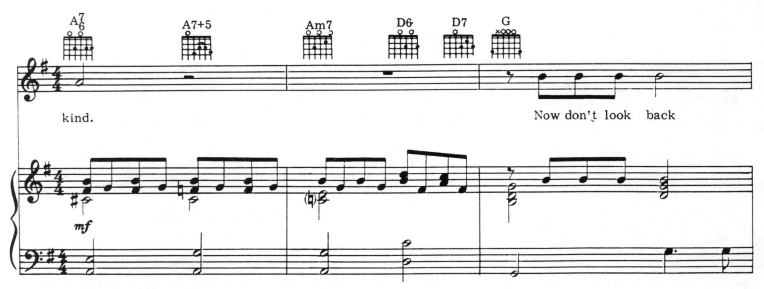

kind. Now don't look back

One of a Kind - 4 - 1

ness this time. If old mem-'ries—— ev - er cloud—— your mind, I'll wish you

sun - shine. So I'll drink this

toast to you: go and find who means the most to you.

But some-night when she's ly - ing close to you, I'll ease through your mind.

One of a Kind - 4 - 4

Recorded by TAMMY WYNETTE

YOU AND ME

Words and Music by
BILLY SHERRILL and GEORGE RICHEY

I can hear the rain, it's fall-ing soft-ly
When he touch-es me, I feel your fing-ers.

As I watch him ly-ing next to
And each time we kiss, I see your

there. Then you'll lock the

door be-hind us, and in my dreams the world can't find us.

It will be so real to me. It's fin-al-ly

you and me.

You and Me - 4 - 4

Recorded by TAMMY WYNETTE

YOU MAKE ME WANT TO BE A MOTHER

Words and Music by
BILLY SHERRILL and NORRIS WILSON

You Make Me Want to Be a Mother - 3 - 1

Recorded by TAMMY WYNETTE

YOUR GOOD GIRL'S GONNA GO BAD

Words and Music by
GLENN SUTTON and BILLY SHERRILL

Your Good Girl's Gonna Go Bad - 3 - 1

Recorded by TAMMY WYNETTE

WOMAN TO WOMAN

Words and Music by
BILLY SHERRILL

Moderate (Triple Feeling)

If you think you got your
If you think you keep your

man in the palm of your hand,
man with a gold — en wed-ding band,

you bet-ter lis-ten.
you bet-ter lis-ten.

Woman to Woman - 5 - 1

Recorded by TAMMY WYNETTE

'TIL I CAN MAKE IT ON MY OWN

Words and Music by
TAMMY WYNETTE, BILL SHERRILL
and GEORGE RICHEY

Verse 5:

But 'til then, Lord, you know I'm gonna need a friend.
'Til I get used to losing you, let me keep on using you,
'Til I can make it on my own.

'Til I Can Make It on My Own - 3 - 3

Recorded by TAMMY WYNETTE

REACH OUT YOUR HAND
(And Touch Somebody)

Words and Music by
BILLY SHERRILL and TAMMY WYNETTE

Reach Out Your Hand - 3 - 1

54

Reach Out Your Hand - 3 - 3

Recorded by TAMMY WYNETTE

HE LOVES ME ALL THE WAY

Words and Music by
BILLY SHERRILL, NORRIS WILSON
and CARMOL TAYLOR

He Loves Me All the Way - 3 - 1

Way. _____ I'm not ev-er gon-na wor-ry a-bout to-mor-row

as long as he makes ev-'ry-thing al-right to-day.

I'd rath-er won-der a lit-tle an' have his lov-in', 'cause when he loves me, He

Loves Me All The Way. _____ when he loves me, He Loves Me All __ The

Way. 'Cause when he loves me, He Loves Me All __ The Way.

Recorded by TAMMY WYNETTE

I DON'T WANNA PLAY HOUSE

Words and Music by
BILLY SHERRILL and GLENN SUTTON

I Don't Wanna Play House - 3 - 2

F7 Eb Bb F7
I've watched Mom - my and Dad - dy and if that's the way it's
mp
Bb7 Tacet Eb
done, I don't wan - na play house It makes my Mom - my
f
Bb F7
cry, 'Cause when she played house my Dad - dy said Good -
mp
1. 2.
Bb Tacet Eb Bb
bye." "I don't wan - na play house bye."
f
rit.

Recorded by TAMMY WYNETTE
(Let's Get Together)
ONE LAST TIME

Words and Music by
BILLY SHERRILL and GEORGE RICHEY

(Let's Get Together) One Last Time - 3 - 1

(Sung:)

You love ___ her, ___ I love ___ him; ___
She loves ___ you, ___ He loves ___ me, ___

___ but here we ___ are, ___ the mu-sic's ___ soft, ___
___ to-mor-row ___ night ___ just won't be ___ right; ___

___ the lights are ___ dim. ___ Let's get to-geth-er one last
___ we won't be ___ free. ___ Let's get to-geth-er one last

Warner Bros. Publications has STAR POWER!

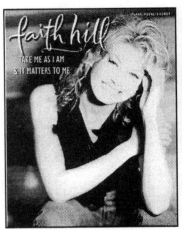

★ PERSONALITY BOOKS
(Piano/Vocal/Chords unless noted)

Michael Bolton/Greatest Hits 1985-1995
(3530A)

Jim Brickman/By Heart
(PF9542) Piano Solos

Garth Brooks/Fresh Horses
(PF9558)

Vince Gill/Souvenirs
(PF9611)

**Don Henley/Actual Miles:
Don Henley's Greatest Hits**
(PF9610)

**Faith Hill/Take Me As I Am &
It Matters to Me**
(PF9616)

**Bruce Springsteen/
The Ghost of Tom Joad**
(PF9609)

Bruce Springsteen/Greatest Hits
(PF9541)

Shania Twain/The Woman in Me
(PF9544)

Dwight Yoakam/Gone
(PF9605)

★ MOVIE SOUNDTRACKS
(Piano/Vocal/Chords)

**Twister – Music from the
Motion Picture Soundtrack**
(PF9628)

**Waiting to Exhale –
Motion Picture Soundtrack**
(PF9603)

★ MIXED FOLIOS
(Piano/Vocal/Chords)

30 Favorite TV Hits
(MF9623)

30 Great Country Songs
(MF9624)

30 Popular Love Songs
(MF9622)

Biggest Country Hits of '95-'96
(MF9628)

Biggest Pop Hits of '95-'96
(MF9627)

Great Popular Songs from the '80s and '90s
(MF9619)

The Great American Torch Song
(MF9611)

Rockin' Country
(MF9609)

The Sensational '50s
(MF9603)

The Sensational '60s
(MF9604)

The Sensational '70s
(MF9605)

The Sensational '80s
(MF9606)

★ GUITAR PERSONALITY BOOKS
(Authentic Guitar-Tab unless noted)

Better Than Ezra/Deluxe
(PG9617)

Garth Brooks/Fresh Horses
(PG9559)

Collective Soul/Collective Soul
(PG9536)

Eagles/Acoustic Classics, Volume 1
(PG9615)

Eagles/Acoustic Classics, Volume 2
(PG9616)

Everclear/Sparkle and Fade
(PG9624)

Garbage/Garbage
(PG9626) Guitar/Vocal Edition with Tablature

Gin Blossoms/Congratulations I'm Sorry
(PG9631)

Green Day/Insomniac
(PG9556)

Iron Maiden/The X Factor
(PG9604)

Alan Jackson/The Greatest Hits Collection
(PG9553) Guitar/Vocal Edition with Tablature

**Carlos Santana/Dance of the Rainbow
Serpent, Volume 1: Heart**
(PG9538)

**Carlos Santana/Dance of the Rainbow
Serpent, Volume 2: Soul**
(PG9539)

**Carlos Santana/Dance of the Rainbow
Serpent, Volume 3: Spirit**
(PG9540)

Bruce Springsteen/The Ghost of Tom Joad
(PG9605)

Toadies/Rubberneck
(PG9619) Guitar/Vocal Edition with Tablature